Abi Palmer is a mixed-media artist and writer. Her work often includes themes of disability, gender and multisensory interaction. Her artworks include: *Crip Casino*, an interactive gambling arcade parodying the wellness industry and institutionalised spaces, displayed at the Tate Modern and Somerset House; and *Alchemy*, a multisensory poetry game, which won a Saboteur Award in 2016. She has written for BBC Radio, *The Guardian* and *Poetry London*. *Sanatorium* is her first book.

PUBLISHED BY PENNED IN THE MARGINS
Toynbee Studios, 28 Commercial Street, London E1 6AB
www.pennedinthemargins.co.uk

First published 2020

Printed in the United Kingdom by TJ International

ISBN
978-1-908058-71-3

The author gratefully acknowledges the support of Arts Council England.

Supported using public funding by
ARTS COUNCIL
ENGLAND

Sanatorium

Abi Palmer

Penned in the Margins
LONDON

San
ator
ium

Have you ever noticed that when we're near water I want to fuck? Remember Snowdonia? That icy river? Me stripping down and unfolding into oblivion while you shrivelled up and waited for it to be over. I was in so much ecstasy it has taken me years to notice you weren't right there with me.

〰

The problem is not that I'm constantly in pain, but that pain wakes me constantly. When I have not slept, I am prone to the following: fatigue, brain fog, paralysis, temporary blindness, floating, climbing out of my body, mid-air encounters with a long-deceased and beloved Carmelite saint.

My body is having an opiate crisis. I have been trying so hard to stay tethered to the ground. Each pill is a stone. We keep on piling them up: stones and stones and stones in my stomach, all trying to knock me down for long enough to stop the floating.

I purchase an inflatable bathtub from China. It's small and bucket-shaped, designed for city blocks where everyone is forced to remain upright. When I fill it, the water floods over my shoulders, so hot it could melt its own container.

If I get out alone, I will faint. I surround the tub with different-sized chairs, each topped with a cup of iced water to bring me round. I switch off all the lights and turn on an illuminated plastic pyramid. It plays frog noises and whale song on a loop. I think about sticking glow-in-the-dark stars on the ceiling, but this isn't a home — it's all our savings.

I sit, silent and bent-legged, folding my toes until their swollen creases soften. I barely breathe, careful for the skin on my back not to scrape the tub's plastic seams.

In 2008 I moved into a flat with my best friend. We took it in turns to take candlelit baths, accompanied by Radiohead's *OK Computer*. This particular combination of warm water, music and light deprivation led to visual hallucinations which I later understood to be a form of synaesthesia: a rose wilts before my eyes; I fall back into a pool of gelatin; we travel along a series of telegraph wires; doves jump up and down in time with the music.

I once repeated this experiment in my inflatable bathtub, but the water was too hot. Instead of falling rose petals, I found myself surrounded by schools of melting sardines.

~~~

*Oh Teresa Sánchez de Cepeda y Ahumada, drown me
with your thick and sacred thighs.*

Immersing myself in bodies of water is just one of many techniques I have experimented with to ease my chronic pain. I don't know why floating leads to visions. I think it is something to do with amniotic fluid.

In the early 2000s, an advert for flotation therapy suggested that placing yourself in a room-temperature bath, your weight supported by Epsom salts, is the closest you will get to being in the womb.

Flotation, the ad explained, is like finding yourself in a pre-birth dreamspace. It's a good way to recover from trauma, because it's a memory of what it's like to exist before trauma can hurt you. The argument goes that flotation eases physical pain because you have reminded your body what it is like to live without it.

My birth was particularly traumatic. I was born via C-section but the surgeon did not count on the lumpy scar tissue around my mother's previous Caesarean wound. They cut the hole too small. When they pulled me out, my head got stuck. An emergency alarm sounded as I began screaming and my body went blue.

≈

When I am instructed to picture a safe space I envisage a deep well, full to the brim with icy water into which I have been thrown. But do not worry: I will survive. I lie back and sink into the water, sucking oxygen through the fat gills at my neck.

When I was seven, doctors watched me drag my feet up and down a grey linoleum floor. They decided that getting my head stuck at birth must have triggered a brain haemmorage, which prevented my neural pathways from connecting properly to my legs.

"Her brain is working very hard," the doctors said to my mother. "No wonder she gets so tired."

At 17 I became so exhausted that I could not lift my body from its bed.

When I was 21, the doctors decided instead that my mobility problems were due to a genetic connective tissue disorder. This, incidentally, would have also caused my mother's abnormal scarring (which led to my head getting stuck in the first place).

When I was 27, I was hospitalised with feet and one knee the size of cantaloupe melons. I was diagnosed with an autoimmune disorder, seemingly unrelated to the above conditions.

The doctors said it was lucky the swelling got so bad or they would have continued to attribute the increased pain and stiffness to one of my other conditions, and refuse appropriate treatment.

They told me not to let myself get too stressed about things, or my condition would get worse.

They suggested I take up swimming.

PART ONE

In 2017 I received funding to attend a thermal water-based rehabilitation programme in Budapest, Hungary.

The Sanatorium was on an island in the middle of the Danube. By day we bathed in mineral-rich thermal water, in a series of 10-minute increments. Between bathing, we took prescribed therapies. My prescribed treatments were: Medical Massage, Underwater Massage, Magnetic Therapy and Underwater Gymnastics.

Every night I was wheeled through a heated underground tunnel to an interconnected building, The Margaret Island Grand Hotel. It's an opulent, multi-tiered structure, built not long after Strauss composed his famous waltz, *The Blue Danube*. Sometimes, when my eyes were tired, I thought I could see the ghost of the hotel's early guests: pale women in opulent gowns with their hair piled high and pinned with flowers; mustachioed men sipping tea in their elegant tailored hats.

Other times I would move so slowly, I became convinced that the entire building had sunk.

Well hi, this is Abi. I've just had my first day of rehabilitation. I've been at the hotel for a couple of days now, with my partner, Hans. He left last night, so today was my first day alone. I've got a carer, Lucy, staying nearby, but yeah, it's a pretty weird feeling, ha ha ha. I'm suddenly realising I'm going to be mainly on my own for the next month, just focusing on my body. I suppose my body is such a significant part of my life that it's always somewhere close to the front of my mind. But it's been five years since the last time I was able to stop and look after it.

I first went to rehabilitation five years ago. It was probably the biggest disappointment of my life. They spent so long lowering my expectations, telling me what I couldn't have. One of the group sessions was about washing a bath. "Imagine you're trying to do your housework. You can't wash your whole bath because you're in too much pain. What do you do?"

I said, "Well, you could talk to social services about whether you need more help to cope with things, couldn't you?"

"Don't expect help," they said. Just wash half the bath.

I was 23. It was my 23rd birthday.

The Sanatorium is different to NHS rehab. First of all, I'm in a private hotel room, not a ward of 20. It's got a giant, king-sized bed, with huge, cushy pillows and blankets. It's the dead of winter but it's so warm, I actually have to use air conditioning. There's a minibar and an unusual number of cupboards. I guess they're used to having people stay for over a month. I've got the Gideon Bible in Hungarian, German and English, in case I feel the need to top myself in any of those languages. That's a good thing to have in a place like this.

You get three therapies a day, give or take. In between, you go and lie in the sulphurous water, which is meant to be really healing. It's the thing people come all this way for. It smells like rotten eggs.

Hans was here for the first few days and we tried the sulphurous water together. It really stinks. On the first day he asked me, "Do you think we'll ever get used to this?"

But by the second day we were in love with it. It's incredibly soothing, just lying around in water that smells like farts. It really does ease your pain. There's one little hosepipe that the real smell comes from, but it's the best part of all. People politely queue at the pipe and take it in turns to hose their aching shoulders. You get used to the smell. You can get used to anything.

The main demographic here is older women. They all get

into the thermal baths in full make-up, with beautiful lipstick and manicures, which is the most perplexing thing to me. When you're steaming the shit out of yourself, why would you do that? They look so perfect and I'm just this little acne-faced kid with a self-trimmed fringe. It turns into a mullet within about three minutes in the steam. My self-esteem isn't particularly high. Maybe that's why they do it, for their self-esteem. Maybe they've been doing this for longer than me.

Today, I had an underwater massage. I sat in a giant blue bath. They told me to grab onto the handrails and trapped my head in a sling. I held on for dear life while a woman silently hosed every inch of my muscles and joints. I don't know if I liked it. I wanted to be sick.

Then there was the Medical Massage. They told me to take off my top, then my bra. I lay on a massage table, almost naked, with my head in a hole. The masseuse took hold of my knickers and pulled them right down, like I was being punished. Then, out of nowhere, she parted my buttocks.

I don't know why she did that. Maybe she was just being thorough. If I'm entirely honest, my hips are hurting a lot less than usual at this point. But I've never had somebody stare so intimately at my arsehole.

And I have really bad gut problems at the moment, ha ha ha. I'm due to be tested for Crohn's disease when I get home — I struggle with eating at the best of times. But they've got loads of healthy food options here and I became so caught up in the beautiful displays of fruit and vegetables that I forgot that I don't digest healthy options very well. I've just basically been shitting the whole weekend. It's been really painful, all blood and jelly in my shit.

After Hans left, I travelled through the underground corridor. I found myself in a room full of tiny cages. Each cage was filled with a single bird. Many of the birds were prize-winners, bearing row upon row of bright rosettes. But they didn't seem happy. Their feathers were patchy and moth-eaten, almost as if they'd already been killed and stuffed. But they kept on moving, all of them chirping frantically, hopping forwards and backwards on tiny perches, or spinning and spinning on the spot. It was raining outside. The spinners all moved at different speeds, wings tucked in, tails knocking bars. The exhibit was sponsored by a birdseed company. When I went back the next day to find it, the entire room had disappeared.

I am withdrawing from opiates. It isn't as bad as I thought it would be (although all week I have been clenching my buttocks, in the race to the bathroom). A few times, I've been up all night, partly due to pain, partly just sweating. In the end, it wasn't the doctor who screamed at me, or the one who told me that I could sell my medication to prisons, who persuaded me to stop me taking them. They just weren't working anymore. Late at night I was always somehow still awake, still painfully aware of my aching back.

≋

I am so full of sickness, it swells my feet. I can't fasten my boots. Sickness spills out of my shoes and forms droplets on the pavement, following me around. You can always trace me, through forests and corridors and under arches. It is impossible to get lost under all this sickness. It hangs off me, my tangled armpits; the shopping bags under my eyes are full to the brim of sickness. You can see it in the roots of my hair and the blisters around my groin.

Today I got out of the lift on the wrong floor and found myself in a dusty, deserted corridor that appeared to have been closed for centuries. The carpet was threadbare. At the end of the corridor, I saw a white thing move. It could have been a stray holidaymaker in their regimental bathrobe. But I'm not so sure. The corridors here are so old and silent.

You could probably live in the bathtub if you wanted to. As I let the water out, I sit, watching the sides implode, feeling gravity and pain return to my body inch by inch. I consider retreating with the water, slipping down the plughole to follow it, or else folding down into the empty bucket, closing the top around me like the petals of a cartoon flower.

My second therapy of the day was listed as underwater gymnastics, which is physiotherapy in water.

It felt a bit like a military regimen. First the physiotherapist told me to march up and down, in time with the whistle. Then we worked on hip strengthening. I had to extend my leg out to the side and in again, sharply, like a pair of scissors.

Then she told me to climb up the steps in the water, one step at a time: step up, step down, switch legs.

After I had done it a few times, I could feel my left knee screaming at me. I said to the physio, "Is it okay if we stop this one?"

It was an interesting moment. I have been in and out of rehabilitation facilities my entire life. I've been very explicitly trained to articulate my physical limitations to physiotherapists, to tell them when something doesn't feel right, or it hurts. The general mantra is: *You Know Your Body Best*. But I thought I saw a flash of something pass across her eyes. It felt like defiance, like maybe she isn't used to being told *No*. I'm worried she's marked me out as a troublemaker. I don't know what I'm going to do about that.

I am so weak at the moment. The form of arthritis I have is called psoriatic arthritis. It's an autoimmune disease. If I overexert myself or get too stressed, my joints get hot and swell up again. Like this [inflates cheeks] ha ha.

The way you treat inflammatory arthritis is to kill your immune system. Every week I inject myself with a chemotherapy drug. The first few months of taking it, I couldn't work because it made me puke. Recently it's been affecting my memory. I keep forgetting what day it is or where I'm going.

But anyway, the idea is that chemo limits the flares in my joints. It's definitely better. But it's never managed to stop the pain entirely. I've still got this one knee that refuses to calm down. When it starts getting angry, the rest of my lower limbs inflate, one joint at a time, until I can't put a toe on the floor without screaming. My biggest fear about coming to the Sanatorium is getting into a flare that spirals out of control.

≋

Let us raise a glass now to Saint Teresa of Ávila, a mystic so pure that she kept floating off to heaven. Nuns had to sit on her stomach to stop her from levitating clean off into the sky.

Today, I've started to make more friends. I had dinner with a group of Egyptians.

They have taken me on as their little pet. They're lovely people, all of them, but because I use my scooter and I'm young and by myself, they want to help me. Two of them have been following me around and helping me pick food from the buffet.

There's one older woman named Zara. When I first saw her, I thought, *Wow, she doesn't look good for 50.* She was quite open about how often she goes to health spas and I started to panic. Something about prunes and, *bloody hell, maybe I shouldn't spend too long in this water.* Then it turned out that she was 72. So maybe the water isn't so bad after all. She looks amazing. Not great for 50, but amazing for 72.

She was so mobile. I would kill to be that mobile. She manages her arthritis by travelling to different resorts around the world. It's a thrice-yearly ritual — Cannes, The Black Sea, Budapest. At each destination she meets up with a selection of friends. Some of them were here: six glamorous Egyptian women in diamond earrings and swimsuits. And a handsome young assistant to push the eldest lady's wheelchair. Between bathing they eat out and go to the opera.

I spoke to another woman today who has been coming to the Sanatorium every year for 30 years; this same rehabilitation facility, taking the waters. She told me she was diagnosed with arthritis when she was 40. She's been doing rehabilitation for 30 years. She uses a wheelchair. We were talking about what the expectations are from almost a month of your life every year going to rehab. She just said, "Look, it doesn't cure anything. It just eases the pain a little bit." For a while she can move a little bit more freely. That's worth the cost.

One of my first therapies of the morning was Magnetic Therapy. Basically, you lie all wrapped up on a giant magnet. I don't really know what happens. A few things did twitch; I could feel bits of me that hurt the most twitching. I don't know if my muscles just do that anyway or whether it was part of the therapy. I asked her, "What is it? What do you think it does?" and she said, "I just have to believe in it. I come out feeling better, so I just have to believe."

~~~
~~~

I had my first out-of-body experience when I was 15 years old. I lay down for a rest in the middle of the day when it happened. I had lost my virginity the day before. I lost my virginity out of politeness. It was a boy of the same age. He said, "Can I see what sex is like?" and I thought he meant what it was *like*, not what it *is*, so I said yes. Then I felt a sharp pain. I was too surprised to say, "No, no, no, that's not what I meant." He stopped when he felt me wincing. I apologised for the misunderstanding. Later that day he threw a basketball at my head.

≈

The next day I lay down for a rest to think about what had happened. It was very hot. I lay down and my body climbed out of itself. I was floating three feet above my own body. It was the middle of the day and suddenly I was floating around.

I had a sense of wonder at being able to move so freely, untethered from the earth. We had these very old wooden floors, and I was floating over them, three feet above the ground, looking at things in my room. I felt so incredibly hot. Every inch of my body was on fire, like there were bubbles coming from out of me. I was so hot. I picked up a glass to drink and the water turned to steam and evaporated from my tongue.

I tried to ask for help and couldn't move. I became aware of my other body, earthbound and paralysed on the bed. I kept jumping between bodies. I tried to scream. I couldn't. I tried to drink and it kept evaporating, over and over again.

≋

When I eventually did come round, I felt so much heavier and confused. None of my limbs were where I thought they would be. Everything was a few inches out. I thought I had been touching myself but suddenly found my hand inches away, on my thigh.

≋

I opened my eyes but I could only see a tunnel. I tried to call my mum using the dial tones. When I was younger, I had composed songs using the dial tones of each button, so I could do Beethoven's Ninth and 'Happy Birthday' through the phone. By knowing the tones, I was able to determine what the number was. I called my mum in her office and she wasn't there, but my aunt answered and I said, "I've got a terrible fever, I'm so hot, water keeps evaporating from my tongue, I can't drink anything."

I went back to the bedroom and the cup wasn't there — it had never existed.

Hi, this is Abi. It's Day Three of being in the Sanatorium. I'm starting to go a little bit mad. I'm starting to get the hang of things. I've realised that time is just a series of 10-minute increments. You wake up. A carer brings you eggs. You have help packing for the day because you're very tired. You reverse out of the door in your mobility scooter and cringe at the loud beeps. You press for the lift to take you down to the ground floor, and you pull back because you've been electrocuted. You go into the reception and a friendly hostess gives you towels.

You take 10 minutes to prepare to go into the water. You put your swimsuit on, you put on all the creams that protect you from things like chlorine, because you don't want to get cystitis, and then you get into the hot, smelly, eggy water for 10 minutes.

You float around, sometimes you stretch, always keeping an eye on the clocks. There are two clocks facing either side of the pool, so no matter where you are, you can look at them. Their times are slightly off. One's a little bit faster than the other, so I tend to go by the clock that faces the entrance.

You float around for 10 minutes. You get out, dry off, maybe sit around for 10 minutes. I don't sit so much, because of worrying about being in wet underwear and getting cystitis. Either I go to a different pool where I sit in chlorine for 10 minutes and try do some exercise, before returning to the eggy, chlorine-free pool (10 minutes) or I go to the changing rooms. I wash myself off. I give myself 10 minutes to wash. I wash myself carefully. I wipe all the water from my delicate genital areas because, no, I do not want to get cystitis.

Then you make your way in your wet bikini top and your new dry pants to the therapies area. In the therapies area, you have 10 minutes. It's a quiet, velvet-chaired room with the only view of the outdoors you see all week. You pour yourself a cup of tea. There's peppermint some days; sometimes there's camomile.

Today there was lemon balm. You drink your tea for 10 minutes, wondering which door your therapist will come through. The therapist inevitably forgets that you're there, so then you remind them of your presence. Then, a few minutes later, your therapist calls you. You get either 20 or 30 minutes of therapy.

~~~

When Teresa was particularly close to the Lord, she would lie so still they believed she was dead. A Sister would hold a candle over her face. If she breathed, the flame would flicker. More than once, she woke from her communion to find little droplets of melted wax on her eyelids.

﹌

Over the coming years, I would find myself jumping increasingly between hallucinations where anything seemed possible to a reality that was increasingly defined by the things my body couldn't do: lift myself from a bed, wash myself, walk more than a few paces. The two states seemed oddly intertwined, each trip out of my body bringing me back down to earth harder. I would land paralysed, blinded, and with a slurring tongue, unable even to describe my own terror. I felt as though gravity was punishing me for all that extra floating.

Today I had a Medical Massage. I forgot to show the masseuse the little note that says to be careful with my joints. He was pretty rough; he had the gropey, under-oiled, over-handsy feel of someone who's watched massage in porn, but doesn't really know how to do it. I can imagine him coming home to a lover and saying, *Oh yeah, I'm trained in massage...*

I think massage took 30 minutes. At that point, I took 10 minutes to have a cup of tea, lemon balm again, probably my third cup of the day. Today has been the first day I was hungry. I haven't shat any blood or jelly for a day, so I ate two eggs, two boiled eggs. I sat around in my towel, a little bit oily from the massage, and then I thought, *"Oh, I've got 10 minutes"*, so I went back into the sulphur pool. I relaxed my muscles after the Medical Massage and tried to recover from what was actually quite a painful experience. I floated around for 10 minutes.

I got out and I prepared myself to go into the chlorine pool for underwater gymnastics. I get really bad skin reactions from chlorine; terrible rashes that get infected and keep me up all night, so I coat myself as much as possible in a layer of Vaseline.

It was a different therapist today and she took a different approach, which I have titled Pushing Me Too Hard™. Yesterday, one of the kindly ladies who have taken me under their wing was bragging about how far she pushes herself during her thrice-yearly rehabilitation experience. Forgetting I have a connective tissue disorder, I thought I'd try it. I just let this woman push me and push me and push me until I was wincing from the pain in my left knee, which is where a lot of the agony lies. We were pushing my muscles so hard. She did this thing where she got one of those inflatable noodles and you had to hold it and push it down under the water, so backwards weight-lifting.

There were a few movements that were really nice. I had to stretch my arms around in the water. It felt almost balletic, like I wanted to dance, but the therapist didn't let me. I'm not allowed to point my toes. I'm not allowed to make it fashion. You have to sort of flap around and not be too poised. But poise helps me learn things, like where to stop before overextending my elbows. Remembering to point a finger or point some toes is a marker of where bodies are supposed to end.

After it was over, I had 10 minutes. I sat in the sulphur water. I thought I'd better not sit in my wet bikini too long because you shouldn't sit in a wet bikini too long if you don't want to get cystitis. I don't want to get cystitis. So then I went back to my hotel room. I got into the shower. I washed myself with another emollient in order to prevent cystitis and limit my psoriasis. Then I sat naked as a pig and ceased to exist because I no longer had 10-minute increments to think about. I sat around and looked at nothing from 3.30pm to 6pm. This feels like an appropriate time to have dinner.

I'm really starting to merge with the water. I'm proud of having made it into the sulphur pool four times today. I could have stayed in there longer. I feel more comfortable in my amphibian form, this slippery self. I like the bit after you leave the hot sulphur water where you climb into icy-cold pebbly water and step slowly, marking a little oval shape with your swollen toes, balancing over rocks.

≈

Floating opens up a world in which I can move with relative ease, where gravity becomes less of an obstacle and where I can see, think and feel with a clarity I do not experience on land. The downside is that I always have to return to a waterless space.

$\approx$

The same is true of sleep-floating. I rise out of my body and start climbing around the sky. It is incredibly erotic, like having a perpetual orgasm. Whenever I've been tethered to earthbound sexuality, particularly where men were involved, there's a distinct end point. But this goes on and on. I don't have to worry about the logistics of my own limbs, the logistics of dislocation. It's tender. It's feminine.

I was able to manifest the most splendid sequences of women-fucking, long before I'd ever thought about trying it on earth.

The biggest question was how to maintain this state of ecstasy. I read a book about lucid dreaming and it told me to spin, to spin and spin and spin, until I found perpetual motion. And so I span, like those floating helicopters we threw when we were children, and that's how I knew that the rules had changed, because when I span, instead of landing slowly and gracefully on the ground, my tulle skirts waving, I found myself to be lifted. My helicopter arms were falling upwards. I found myself empty of gravity. And without the means to fall or tip over, I kept on spinning, in ecstasy forever. And through the spinning I became a kinetoscope, projecting moving images from my mind; the most fantastic things! I could create moving beasts! And visions, and women dressed like genies who touched and whispered and put their hands on me. And all the while I knew it wasn't real, and I let them do anything. Things I didn't know you could even do. Until I didn't know it wasn't real. And then it was a jolt of terror, one moment spinning and the next moment stuck in my adolescent bedroom, unable to reach the phone. And I asked the nuns to stop touching me because someone I loved might walk in any moment and find me compromised. But they didn't hear me. I couldn't move my tongue! Each time I thought it might be over, somewhere else, another part of me had snapped and kept on spinning. And the helicopter leaf is split into two blades, each pointing in a different direction. One part of me moving and the other stuck fast. Two paths, and somehow I'm following both at the same time. Both of them are sticky with sap.

Everyone's very well made-up and poised in the dining hall. I wonder what they'd do if I didn't dress right. When I'm in a room by myself for long periods of time, I give myself these makeovers that are designed for other people, and then I look at myself in the mirror and feel really good. Then I take all the make-up off and then I go about my business. I've started doing it here. Putting on a face to remind myself I have one. I was late for dinner.

It's the first time in days that I've felt able to eat. On my way along the thermal-heated corridor, somebody recommended I try the salmon. I didn't sit with anyone else. I wanted to be alone. I helped myself to the salmon, but also some chicken and some bacon. The bacon was wrapped around a bit of turkey breast. I ate with such speed and ferocity; a violence towards my meal that was almost obscene. After that, I left my plate with my knife and fork very firmly not closed, lest anyone think I had finished. I stormed to the grapes table because grapes are a fruit I can eat without shitting myself, so I thought I better claim them. I stormed over to the dessert table and claimed a chocolate cream. I stormed back and shovelled salad into my face until it was time to shove grapes into my face, then shove in the chocolate. I drank a lot of water.

Then I sat with my notebook and listened to the orchestra. Have I told you about the orchestra? There are five musicians here, serenading you as you eat. It's really grand in the dining hall;

all wood panelling and chandeliers. Every night they play one of Vivaldi's *Seasons*, the one the Job Centre use when they put you on hold. They play *The Blue Danube*. Tonight they played 'What A Wonderful World'. I like watching how they talk to each other and move with each other. They take it in turns to play songs and take rests. And there I am, just wolfing down food.

Yesterday, one of the Egyptian ladies warned me against applauding, because when you clap the musicians come to your table and serenade you individually. And then you find yourself buying their records. She said this had happened to her five times and she bought five CDs. Eventually she stopped clapping and they stopped coming over and she stopped buying their music.

There's a lemon tree on my balcony. I've had it for years. Once, a summer after we got it, it started weeping sticky tears, and I didn't know why. At first I was disgusted. Then I was terrified. Eventually I learned about scale insects, sucking on each leaf's underbelly, leaving gaping holes that the plant tries to heal. I nursed it back to health, but since then it has faced intruder after intruder: aphids, whitefly, mites. Each time a new creature decides to invade, the tree wilts more quickly, losing its leaves, growing them back stunted and curling. It looks like it is in constant pain. I empathise, I really do.

I become obsessed with hunting them down, these new diseases, scouring the internet for cures, Googling signs that it is either dying or could be cured. One year we tried a reliable pesticide but the next year I became worried about the bees.

A few years ago, Hans suggested giving up and throwing it out, making way for a better plant. I couldn't hear it. I wept at him for a whole weekend. The idea of abandoning this old lady, who had been hurt and fought back to health so many times, seemed violent, cruel. "This is our baby," I shouted. "This is all we have." He was horrified by my frenzy and did not offer suggestions about the tree again. She became mine. He cares less about the garden.

Each time I refuse to kill her, she grows a little. Her flowers bloom and smell fragrant. One day I saw a bee kissing them. I fed her citrus feed and calcium pebbles. Every now and then she begins to bear fruit but it feels like the effort nearly kills her. Once, after a hot day, I came home to find a tiny, green-yellow lemon beside her on the ground. She sat in silence.

My right knee has a sore. I don't know how. I coat it in thick layers of oily nappy-rash cream and try not to panic. In the thermal bath, the sting of sulphur makes it impossible to ignore. I am aware of my skin's tightness, of each movement under the surface.

The abrasion is its own planet, its red crust swollen and magnified. I move through the water, wincing, aware of how the mound of white cream stands out, and how many of my fellow bathers are watching. I scan their faces for disgust or displeasure at sharing my germs. Then I worry about their germs. I lift my knee a little higher and look for a ring around the wound site. Too early to tell.

A yellow layer forms over the surface. Later, when I look again, it has disappeared. At first I worry that I have knocked it off into the water and I want to be sick. Then I worry that maybe the acid of the bath has dissolved it. And if it's doing that, is it dissolving my skin?

Our entire balcony begins to die. Vine weevils the size of my fingernails crawl indoors and we find them gnawing holes in the orchid. One hot night, we go outside to hunt them and instead find thick, fat slugs trailing up and down our bulbs and burrowing into the ivy. I take my bag of Epsom salts and scatter it over the hot ground. I lay beer traps and nematodes. Next come black flies. I don't know what they are. And caterpillars, gluing whole leaves together. And fungus gnats. And sooty mould. It is almost aphid season and I know what's coming. I cannot cope with this plague of intruders. *A home garden does not need to be perfect*, I read in a gardeners' manual, late at night. We stop going outside after I tread on a dying slug. Eventually I cry again and ask Hans to sweep up the salt because the whole scene is too stressful. I stop looking out the window. I want to buy more nematodes and he says, "Whatever you want is fine." We fight for an entire weekend about pest control. "It's not that I want to be right," I say, "it's that I want you to engage without me having to ask you to." When he is not looking, I mouth the words "emotional labour" at a cactus.

I wonder if the water is too salty, if I am allergic to the sulphur, if my skin has shrunk after all that soaking.

      The ecosystem of my skin is so fragile; once the surface is broken, all barriers are down. It's impossible to control who gets to enter and who gets to leave. I look again at my sad little knee and feel sorry for it, all plump and defenceless. Despite the fact they feel so old and creaking, there is something young about my knees. In the summer they get freckles and I pore over them like a child, exclaiming with delight as I discover a new spot. Where did they come from? When do they appear? Here, through the liquid, they expand in bleachy whiteness. I look closer, hoping to spot the intruder: microscopic bugs or little abrasions. I imagine them settling in, sending messages through my nerve endings to complete their command:

THWACK!

I begin having panic attacks about the holes in the balcony's violets. I go to a garden centre and ask for advice. The gardener listens, but is underwhelmed. "Oh yeah," he says, when I tell him about the vine weevil. "We get them too." I watch another gardener peel a slug off the bottom of a plant pot and throw it into the bush she is watering.

"But it's like a plague," I say. "I can't fight all of them. The number of intruders seems disproportionate to the number of growing things."

The gardener thinks. "A strong plant should be able to handle a couple of insects," he tells me. "Weak plants are more vulnerable to attack. That's when an infestation will take over and spread."

It's hard to cry in this sunny garden full of life.

I say, "And if it was really weak and attracting invaders, could one plant be bringing in pests and spreading them to all of the other plants?"

"Yes," says the gardener, spraying a pot. "Exactly."

When I get home, I tell Hans we have to give up the lemon tree.

The next day in underwater gymnastics, we do pull-ups. I bend my knees and feel both of them graze against the rough ceramic wall.

≋

If I were to give advice, I would say to parents that they ought to be very careful whom they allow to mix with their children when young; for much mischief thence ensues, and our natural inclinations are unto evil rather than unto good.

ST TERESA

≈

There came a moment when I realised I was not in complete control of these experiences, and that perhaps I should tread more carefully. I pictured Ezekiel, how the hand of the Lord came upon him, and I knew that I didn't want to feel any master's hand. I took down the crucifixes stolen from my Catholic school classrooms and hung, like trophies on my goth teen walls. I refused to watch *The X-Files* or read about alien abductions. The worst thing, I imagined, would be to assign meaning to my state.

And so I drifted.

≋

Of course sometimes you would struggle not to find meaning. When your body is a stringless puppet, lifted by a giant invisible hand and thrown — THROWN — against the walls, lifted again and hurled to the floor, it doesn't take a genius to understand that you are being punished.

Hello, this is Day Six. It's Saturday morning. I'm in bed, propped up on a giant pillow. I took the liberty of not having breakfast today and asking my carer not to come, so I could have a rest. I have been hoarding cheese and yoghurts from the breakfast buffet all week so I guess, if I get enough energy to lift myself out of bed, maybe I can eat those.

I am broken. Yesterday, my physiotherapist told me it was time to start exercising on land again. She sent me to the gym. I used a recumbent bike on the lowest resistance. I had this sense of strength coursing through my limbs and my back muscles that I haven't had in years. I felt like a well-oiled machine. I did my stretches afterwards like you're supposed to. It's been so long. The old routine just came flooding back.

Today, I'm meant to go back and lie in the sulphur water. It's my rest day, but you're still supposed to bathe for recovery. I'm so tired, all I want to do is lie in bed and watch videos of people opening Kinder Surprises.

Week One has been really interesting. I'm exhausted. I had fun. I didn't expect to have fun and I have. I have been able to take a lot of rest. I've done more exercise than I've done in years. My stomach is still in ruins, but I have managed to eat.

I now sleep wearing a sports bra. I never thought I'd have permission to wear a sports bra.

I'm in a lot of pain, but it's still less pain than I thought I might be in. And I know that if I do go and get back into the hot water, the pain might temporarily go away. Also, if I take, like, a fuck-ton of painkillers, which I'm about to. Thank God for sulphurous water and opiates.

It would be nice to get outside and see sunlight. I haven't seen sunlight for a week now and I miss it. I miss the outdoors. I'm so exhausted.

So yeah, that's where I'm at now. Week One is done. I'll see you at Week Two.

PART TWO

≋

When I bathe, the water turns yellow with sickness; and when we clean the bath afterwards we are washing the sickness away. It sticks to our kitchen sink. Soon the air is clogged with the taste of sickness, more pungent and noxious. When other people come into my house they faint. I have to blow on their eyelashes to rouse them and let them make their escape. Pretty soon, the plughole refuses to drain. Sickness has blocked it, waxy and grey. Under the city it swells, a fatberg of sickness floating through the Thames.

The inflatable bathtub begins to get an aroma about it; something mushroomy and thick. It is not entirely unpleasant. Only after I sit in the bath do I notice the dark ring of black forming around the rim. I try so hard not to let my shoulders brush against it. I hope that you fail to notice me now, surrounded by filth and fungus. As my cartilage melts in the water, I see the liquid around me thickening into gloop, and growing fibrous hairs. White-blue fur sits damp on my tongue and heavy on my cheekbones, my fat knees. The bathtub is full to the brim with spores. I watch them grow, flattening out from papery threads into thick and coiling mushrooms, so dense and spongy I can barely move. Mushrooms springing out of my arms! Springing out of my neck! Mushrooms between my legs; fat white mushrooms, thick and spongy. My toes are mushrooms. A moist old grey one crumbles into mush.

The image fades. I sink my body deeper into the water. I do not return to the bathtub for a long time.

≋

When I climb out of my body, it doesn't always happen as easily as the first time. Sometimes, the pressure of moving between one world and another is incredibly uncomfortable. It's like every blood vessel in my body is fighting to keep me here, like it doesn't want to let me go. I feel them squeezing and squeezing as I lift out of my body, but then they pull me back. It's like clenching to go to the toilet. You lift as if to release, but it doesn't come. I feel my own body push against itself. I feel my spirit push against the edges of my body and beg to leave and then my body pulls it back. I beg to leave and it pulls me back.

I keep forgetting to tell anyone about the fungus (or maybe I don't want to, I am quite ashamed). Eventually, one night I strip down to my knickers. I work on the bathtub myself with a sponge and a bottle of Fairy liquid. Dead skin flakes have gathered around the base near the plughole. I scrub and scrub. My arms ache and my back is buckled, but I do not stop until the room is full of suds. I run the shower over it until the water runs clear.

I dry it down as you would a baby suffering from nappy rash, tenderly wiping between every fold. I resolve to add 'cleaning the bathtub' to the ritual of washing. But I can't follow through. I find myself wet and dizzy, more often than not, flopped on the bed in a damp towel, waiting for someone to get me dressed.

I attempt to expand my bathing ritual into being cleaner, scrubbing myself down before I climb in. But this proves to be impractical. Either I scrub before I fill the bathtub, then wait for an hour, shivering and exhausted; or else I fill the bathtub first — then there is nowhere for the shower water to run. I read funny memes about white people who do not know how to clean themselves properly. Certainly, I am one of the worst offenders. It shows: the filmy layer of scum around me, my unwashed legs.

In Bernini's statue *The Ecstasy of Saint Teresa*, she is lying back in a swoon with her mouth wide open. An angel stands over her. In one hand he holds an arrow, directed at her heart; the other teases the hem of her robe. Beams of light erupt from the sky. You can tell from her face she is in both kinds of ecstasy.

When I look at that sculpture, the folds of her marble dress, I can feel her lightness. Breathing life into stone. That is exactly what it means to float.

Today my physiotherapist invited me to leave my mobility scooter upstairs and walk. It was more of a challenge than an invite.

"Why are you still using your wheelchair?" she asked. "If you say your new medication is working, why do you need it?"

"Well that's why I'm here," I said, "to try to increase my mobility."

Psoriatic arthritis isn't my only condition. I was born with a connective tissue disorder. I've been in and out of rehab and wheelchairs and therapies my whole life. In the past I have tried to throw away my wheelchair completely and when my joints have declined again it has always been a disappointing readjustment. Each time I have had to reframe my relationship with my body.

People see a wheelchair as a bad thing. They require time to readjust. They say things like, "I'm so sorry, what HAPPENED?" Family and friends get impatient. I find myself having to justify the way I move.

I tried reasoning with the therapist. I don't think losing my mobility aids is the ultimate aim of my rehabilitation experience. Having wheels is a tool that makes my life easier. I am here to increase my strength and to reduce my pain. But losing the chair entirely will never be an option for my body. Even if I were stronger, I couldn't carry a heavy bag or go further than a set number of steps. When I last felt able to mobilise without a wheelchair, I was unable to go beyond the end of my road. My whole world closed down. I was so busy focusing on not falling that I stopped noticing the space around me.

We moved into a house that is full of ghosts. It had belonged to a family friend, Fleur. She was a laughter therapist. She had been diagnosed with throat cancer after years of the doctor dismissing her symptoms on the grounds that she simply laughed too much. A proud member of the New Age movement, Fleur was obsessed with the healing benefits of blueberries and green tea.

I had felt her haunting me even before she died. On receiving her diagnosis, she made a visit to John of God in Brazil, a 'psychic surgeon' famous for performing surgery on unanesthetised patients while in a trance state and without a medical licence. He later became the subject of one of the largest sex-abuse scandals in Brazil. Even after they sent her home with the recommendation of a hospice, she refused to give up hope. I remember her walking around her flat, blood trailing from her nostrils. "It's the psychic operations," she would murmur. The cancer had spread to her brain.

Long before I understood how my body was failing, I found a photograph of myself in a bag of prayers she had carried to Brazil. She had taken it upon herself to ask a man I did not believe in to psychically cure me of an illness I did not yet know I had. It's like the universe was working backwards and had fallen out of time.

Fleur's flatmate came calling and fell in love with me. I sometimes heard her laughter. We placed our dog's ashes on the mantelpiece. The cat died, was buried, and was dug back up again. Her widow hummed 'What's New Pussycat?' as he dug the grave. I developed an itch all over my body, which nobody could see.

I began hallucinating almost immediately. I hallucinated so often I was weak with it, my tongue heavy, my vision obscured. My mother bought me a little bell to ring when I was coming round, but I was always too weak to reach. I got sicker and sicker.

It must be at around this time that I purchased the white cotton Victorian nightgown. In my out-of-body memory I am always wearing it. It is a perfect thing, so starched and white and floor-length; it hangs in folds. Even without a person in, it floats. It has everything to do with floating.

One day in the bathtub I take a comb and part my leg hair. It occurs to me that women's shaving culture has prevented a whole market in body hair gels and follicle glitter. I do the swirls from Van Gogh's 'The Starry Night'. I think of my acrylics in the next room and wonder if I would ever be able to sit still long enough for painted leg swirls to dry and, if I did, would they become an Instagram sensation and, if they did, what would that prove? Then I remember my childhood propensity for black hole paintings, working in and in to the page till its skin split. I think of my psoriasis. When I dip my legs back into the water, the artwork is instantly washed away.

The tub sags over onto the doorframe, and I accidentally close the door on its leg. It buckles immediately, like a drunk at Christmas. I find myself wincing and clenching my own left knee.

One day my feet are swollen and I trip over the edges of the bath-tub. I curl up beside it on the floor.

This flat was brand new when we moved here. My entire housing column had been reserved for disabled tenants, but in the end I was the only cripple who could afford it. I think I'm the only one the Housing Association has ever met. To adapt the home for disabled people, they had taken out the standard bathtub and fitted an ordinary shower cubicle straight onto the bathroom floor. The shower was so high I couldn't reach it to wash water away from my body. The water pressure was so low it felt like being pissed on. The plughole was in the corner of the shower. Water pooled in the centre of the room, forming a scummy puddle that never dried. The entire room became saturated. The skirting boards swelled with damp and fungus. Cardboard walls expanded into soggy cracks and slid away. We bought a squeegee to wipe the floor clean, but it quickly rusted. Eventually a lady from the council came around. It wasn't good enough, she told me. "You can't just expect a standard shower tray to pose as a regulation wetroom." She ordered a new bathroom, with a shower seat and anti-slip floors.

"I need a bath," I told her. "It's the one thing that keeps me moving when my joints hurt."

"Baths aren't regulation," she told me. "You might not be able to climb into one. You might fall and break your hip."

"But I can climb in," I told her. "A bath makes all the difference."

She ordered the regulation shower. She refused to let me purchase an additional bath.

I collapsed the day we moved in. It was a shock to everybody except me.

I was unable to lift my back properly, or hold my head straight. After a month or so in bed I requested a wheelchair so that I could return to college. The college was infinitely kind, building me a chaise longue on which I could recline and continue to paint. We agreed to slow down my education, working towards one examination at a time.

Other than my twice-a-week college outings, for one hour at a time, I was primarily housebound. I became obsessed with *Vogue* magazine and period dramas. Everything else was too exhausting.

Not having much access to the outside world, I began to lose perspective, dressing myself in charity shop floor-length gowns and placing elaborate pearl arrangements in my hair. It was very painful to lift my arms. After dressing I fell back down exhausted and reclined all day on pillows until it was time to take the pearls out. A carer undressed me at 7pm. I spent between 18 and 24 hours a day in bed.

The care agency chosen by social services maximized their profit by scheduling each minimum-wage worker to visit four houses in the same hour, to wash, dress, feed and clothe each patient. Most of the employees were migrants on freelance contracts. They told me they were often working 12-hour days but only got paid for 8 of them.

One of the support workers was particularly keen on cleanliness. She put me in the bath and scrubbed at my skin with a flannel until it was red and raw. She insisted on washing my genitals. I told her I could do it myself but she refused to let me. She scrubbed so hard that it tore the delicate skin around my labia. I was unable to sit for days.

When the bathroom fitters came, they had to chip away the old wet concrete from the floor. Dust went everywhere: so dry I could hardly breathe. It worked its way into the cracks of my eyelids, puffing them up with lizard scales. Then into the soles of my feet. They swelled into turgid lumps, hot and tender. I felt like a bear with thorns in its paw.

We spent a long time deciding on the colour of anti-slip flooring. It was a hard call between various shades of beige with puke flecks, NHS grey or municipal-swimming-pool blue. In the end we went for Anvil — the closest I could find to pure black. I hoped it would be so dark I would fall right down into it.

We spent almost two years like this, not really knowing whether it might change.

One day I was finally well enough to venture up the attic staircase to my mum's en-suite bathroom. She helped me into the tub. It was so nice to bathe without a support worker, for longer than the 10 minutes allocated by social services.

When I looked up I saw a ghost in the skylight. Her body looked something like my own, but larger, weaker and less elegant than when I saw her last. She was so pale, it was unclear where body ended and the water began.

By the end, my feet were so swollen and full of dust I couldn't walk. I went to stay at a friend's house. It's always such a strange thing, staying with other people and seeing how they live their lives. I am flabbergasted by how easily they do things: get up at sunrise and make their own breakfasts and sit at their desks and go to work, then out with friends for dinner. I was very hungry but couldn't remember how to do anything about it. At night my stomach ached with nothingness.

I sneaked into the kitchen and ate fistfuls of dry corn-flakes, spilling maizey crumbs all over carefully curated floor tiles. I didn't know how to sweep them up. There is so much I do not know. I felt so slow and stupid, sitting alone in the dark, wondering if they could hear me and, if they could, what they might say.

The next day I watched my friend sit at her desk all day and work. As she read through a document, she twisted her hair up into a top knot without looking into a mirror, almost as if she wasn't thinking. Then she turned to tell me about an idea she was having, seeming not to notice how easily it had fallen into place.

I returned home. The wetroom had been completed. The Anvil-black anti-slip floor was stuck fast. I couldn't wait to clean myself. I sat in my new bath chair and let the water fall over me. I was so busy enjoying the sensation of wetness that I didn't look down. I didn't realise the plughole wasn't working until I was ankle-deep in water.

≋

FACT 1

The most flawless reproduction of Van Gogh's famous painting 'The Starry Night' was actually combed into the leg hair of a woman who, it must be noted, has legs for days.

FACT 2

The reproduction was sold through the underground market as the original; signature and all.

FACT 3

The legs have now been hung in a rich, fat business-man's penthouse, but this is his second home, and anyway he travels a lot for work.

≈

This is just as well, as the woman to whom the legs are attached needs to get down sometimes and pace around, to keep the blood flowing. She uncorks his vintage wines and tips them into the sink, one by one. Eventually the businessman notices something and calls an exterminator.

The exterminator has never encountered a case of rodents drinking wine at the top of a gold-plated tower. His eyes lock with those of the woman to whom the legs are attached, but he looks away, saying nothing. He adds an extra zero to the end of his fee.

≋

The legs twitch and find themselves aching for home.

≈

Night after night, the woman to whom the legs are attached stares out at the sky and tries to perfect its swirling, pointing her toes, first this way, then that. Once she turns herself upside down cat-like, convinced that this will force her possessor to notice, and thus more closely resemble the original.

But his sofa faces the other way, and anyway, he does not know much about skies.

≋

The closest he comes to understanding is his down-fall. At lunch, a potential investor happens to mention an interest in fine art. The businessman boasts unabashedly that he possesses one of the most famous paintings in the world.

"I saw it once at the Louvre," says the investor. "I wasn't a fan of the Impressionists before, but, oh my, up close, it almost seems to be moving."

"I know exactly what you mean," says the business-man, thinking back to the time he saw his painting cough.

≈

After this, he cannot stop looking. He spends more time in the apartment, allowing his wife and children to believe he is having an affair. In reality he is standing by the sofa, staring back and forth between legs and ever-changing sky.

Each time he turns, the legs readjust themselves slightly, but the woman to whom they are attached does not dare blink. Consequently her eyes soon begin streaming, a puddle forming on the ebony floor.

≈

The businessman is too busy staring to notice, but his property manager calls a plumber after the tears have leaked onto the ceiling below. The plumber is less astute than the exterminator, but still no idiot. When no source for the leak can be found in the piping, he dips his finger into the salty mixture and tastes it, correctly identifying the liquid as teardrops (but failing to notice an aftertaste of mascara). The businessman incorrectly assumes that the tears are his own.

≈

Not having eaten or slept for months, a short time later the businessman lies on his deathbed. He smiles and with his final breath announces to a room, with nobody left but a pair of legs, attached to a woman, pinned to a creaking wall, that he can die satisfied, knowing he has been moved to tears by a famous work of art.

Week Two, Day Two. Today I am practising at walking. My carer has wrapped me up in seven layers of tights and led me out into the cold October, with my mobility scooter. We head to a running track. I am not sure I am supposed to be here. I have never been able to run.

Once, when I was 15, I read an article in a glossy magazine about how jogging was supposed to be enjoyable. There was a photograph of a slender woman in headphones and yoga pants running through an open field. I wanted to give it a go. Mum tried to teach me. She took me out to a field to practise, shouting things over the long grass, like "Lift your ankles and point your knees." I don't think she knew how to run either. I became painfully aware of my own skeleton, knocking about inside me. The distant tree I was aiming at refused to come nearer. The earth sat against the fat sky, indifferent, refusing to acknowledge my force.

The next day, my knees hurt so much I left school early. I wept little dark stains onto the pavement all the way home.

It is a strange sensation, bearing your body's weight. My feet, in their hi-top shoes and plastic insoles, connect with the surface of the island, all dressed up in a layer of concrete. There is a lot to think about: lifting the slump of my shoulders; pointing my head straight; heel first, remembering knees over toes. I am meant to be listening for signs that I am overdoing it, but the sensation of propelling myself along is intoxicating. The rhythm of foot against pavement — I am euphoric! Beside me, the river races past. I could dive in and join it, but I don't. I see life passing on the other side of the bank.

There is a stabbing in my knee. "Just to the next lamppost," I say to myself. But it won't come nearer. I have slowed down. I am moving underwater like treacle. We stop the timer and rest. When I go back to the hotel, it is late but I make my way back down to the baths, hoping that the sulphur in the water is more effective than my weekly chemotherapy injections.

I deflate the tub and fold it back into the airing cupboard; a room so vast we could hide a secret baby. My carers move my clutter from shelf to shelf, but I take to intruding on their organisational practice to wrap my arms around the pathetic empty husk of deflated PVC.

The tub's skin breaks. My skin breaks.

My hair begins to dissolve in the sulphur, breaking away in my post-bath shower.

In the pool, I notice that my veins have become more prominent.

Sometimes at night, I put out my hand and think my skin is becoming more translucent.

One day I look in the mirror and realise I can see the wall behind my own head.

Before I go to dinner, I apply a layer of foundation. I outline my eyes with kohl and wear much more lipstick than I ever would at home. It occurs to me that I am becoming one of the old women who wear turbans and full make-up in the hot tub. I think I understand why now. It is nice to remember that you have a face.

I leave my room. My mobility scooter beeps as I reverse. I travel through the quiet, carpeted corridors. Lights flicker on as I approach. I turn into the stairwell, bumping the doors with the side of my scooter as I pass. I press the button for the lift. Static electrocutes my hand. I pull my finger away. I wait.

I travel down to the ground floor. As the lift door opens, new arrivals to the hotel bustle all at once, dragging their suitcases out of the scooter's path. I thank them and glide past the little shop displaying cashmere sweaters, the commissary selling chocolate bars and bottled water. I turn smoothly into the reception, its polished wood panelling and mint green carpets, where staff are handing out towels and booking massage appointments. They greet me as I pass.

The air is humid and smells of eggs. I travel further, past a mural depicting a leafy park scene. I find myself by the tiny service elevator. The lighting is very good. I take another selfie.

The lift takes me down to the basement and opens on a small, silent corridor. The floor is paved with brown and white chequered tiles. The walls are bright orange. The air sits warm and humid on my face. There is no natural light. I travel through the underground tunnel at top speed, almost floating. I pass strangers dressed in bathrobes with regulation flip-flops. The walls are lined with a series of large black and white posters showing the history of the spa. The Grand Hotel. Women laughing in their bathing suits, crowds of young soldiers, all big eyes and cheekbones.

At the end of a long labyrinth is another lift, even smaller. I press the button and wait. It takes me back up to the first floor. As I exit the tunnel, a sign points me to The Grand Hotel. I kick my way through a set of swinging doors and find myself in a corridor with taller ceilings, walls in white and peach. Trolley boys go in and out of doors, dressed in red velvet waistcoats and neat little hats. I kick through another door and the scene changes.

A dark, cool, shining room, held up by jade pillars, thick as tree trunks. Everything glistens — the sparkling marble floor, walls lined with mahogany and silk. Spindly antique furniture grouped on rich rugs in tiny clusters, like a 1920s tea room, all silk cushions and low tables. Only the flat-screened television betrays the sense of era.

In the corner, a shining bar, lined with bottles of dark liquor. The drink of the month is hot chocolate with whipped cream and apricot schnapps. A waiter in a black waistcoat and bow tie polishes a brandy glass.

I pass the bar and park my scooter by a mahogany coat rack. "Hello Miss Palmer," says the maître d'. "Table for one?"

I nod. "Yes please," I say. Behind the maître d', the dining hall is low, with warm orbs of orange light hanging from the chandeliers. I make my way towards my normal table but he steers me round.

"A table in the centre tonight," he says. "A woman as beautiful as yourself should always be in the centre." I smile and thank him. I am acutely aware that he knows where I live. Two nights ago, he came to my room to return a misplaced sketchbook.

I do not normally order a drink with my meal, but tonight I am feeling festive. I ask for a glass of red wine and sip it slowly.

By now, I have perfected my buffet routine. I ignore soups completely, but do a single circuit of the space, eyeing the appetiser tray more out of interest than pleasure, the fruit stand (in case of grapes) and checking whether there are any gluten-free chocolate cakes left at the dessert table. I scoop a fruit cup as I pass, then head straight to the salad cart. I pick an entire plate of cucumbers, another plate of undressed iceberg lettuce, a single lemon. I return them to the table. I meander around the proteins, weighing up my choices: fillets of baked turkey, tough steaks and pale, flaky salmon. I go with turkey, layering multiple fillets on my single platter. I don't bother with sauces.

Back at the table, I have run out of hand strength for cutlery. I plant an entire turkey fillet on my fork and chew it slowly, listening to the orchestra.

The quintet is playing a lively jazz number. The pianist is new and the songs seem to have an extra energy to them, the band on their toes as he changes time signatures midway through a piece. They speed up and maintain eye contact with each other. I think of the word *synergy* as I gnaw my cucumber.

After my meat, I work the way through my salad, picking up each piece of lettuce and popping it into my mouth. I reflect on the abundance of pre-sliced cucumber with something close to wonder: the idea that I can eat so much of a vegetable without hurting my stomach, the fact that so much of it is just *there*, readily available! I eat and eat. When it is done, I return to the buffet cart for more turkey and a platter of potatoes. The music is still lively, even faster this time. I join in when everybody applauds, before returning to my dinner — forkful after forkful of meat and carbs.

The next song begins. It's 'Moon River', one of their standards. The orchestra are so in sync, and I think about how unusual it is to see live music like this.

The lead violinist approaches my table and I realise I am in danger of a serenade. I lower my face into my potatoes but it is already too late.

Other diners are turning their heads to look my way. I am not sure what to do with my eyes or my mouth. I spill my potatoes, getting olive oil on my top. I wonder if people will notice I've got so much lettuce and that I'm not very good at chewing. I finish my mouthful and switch to my wine glass, grateful for something to hold.

As the song comes to an end, he adds so much embellishment that he lands on the wrong note.

Everyone claps at the orchestra.

"Thanks," I say.

"Thanks," he says. "Any requests?" he asks.

"No," I say. I think.

"Yes," I say. "I like it when you change time signatures."

He thinks for a moment and returns to the band. A pause, in which they appear to be arguing. But then a song begins. It is lively and unexpected, in what sounds like 5/7. At unexpected moments it shifts gears. The pianist does an excellent solo. People applaud. Then comes the double bass. It's electrifying and strange. Everyone has stopped eating. They watch. The violinist is gearing up. He steps away from his band for a moment. He steps towards my table. He is coming for me.

He forces eye contact so vigorously that I choke on my wine and have to hold my breath. He plays and plays, furiously, as the band speeds up, leaning his body over for emphasis, never failing to lock eyes. As they slow back down again, I try to focus on what the rest of the band is doing, but he's gesturing at me with his head and his elbows and smiling. Everyone is watching but they are looking at him and I barely matter. I wish I were on one of their tables.

The song ends. I applaud, looking at my hands. He does not leave my side.

"That was great," I say.

"Thanks," he says.

"Where are you from?" he asks.

"London," I say. I lift my glass.

Then he says:
        "You are very beautiful."

My face gets hot. The room is no longer watching.
        "Oh," I say. "Thanks."

It's as if I've climbed out of myself. I'm watching in third-person, the room echoing like my head is in a bucket. As my face floods, I am aware of every little detail. The spilled wine on the edge of my lip. The hairs prickling on the back of my neck. I want to get away but I think I am too uncoordinated. I don't know where to put my eyelashes. If I avoid eye contact too quickly, perhaps he will think I'm flirting. I pick up my glass again. I hope I look embarrassed enough for him to leave.

He goes back to the band and I make an effort to stop watching. But he is ever-present. I finish my potatoes.

When I go to collect my second fruit cup, he is there, looking at me. He locks eyes as I pick out my gateau. The orchestra are playing another brilliant song and I want to focus but I don't want to give him the wrong idea. I pull out a notebook to look at.

≈

He asks me to see what sex is like and I say, "Yes," thinking of the dry humping that teenagers do so often do. But he means that he wants to see what sex *is*. I feel a sharp pain and I cry out. "Sorry," I say, "sorry I misunderstood you." Later, he throws a basketball at my head.

He is handing me a drink even though I'm underage. Later I am slurring and he is is rubbing my legs. "One more year," he says, "one more year and you'll be 16." He hands me his wedding ring.

I get up, naked from the bed where we have previously lain. He throws me back to the floor. "No," I say. But he doesn't listen. "No," I say again in the bathroom but again he doesn't listen. I focus my eyes on the ceiling. I think, *one day I will hate you for this.*

I'm standing on stage with a band and a microphone. The stage is the same height as the dirty carpeted floor, and he stands next to me, cupping my left buttock. His girlfriend's dad is paying our bill that night so I do not dare ask him to leave.

I make my way to the bathroom. Withered old faces leer. I want the night to be over.

The orchestra have stopped playing. I make my exit, looking down at the floor. The players are in the atrium, hovering around a low table, rolling cigarettes. I grab my scooter. He stands to greet me. I scoot away as quickly as I can.

There were 17 women on the ward when I went to NHS rehab. Everyone was defined by their proximity to a loving, abled man. They talked about marriage constantly. Women of my age were rehabilitating to walk down the aisle or tolerate their honeymoons. Women my mother's age were preparing to stand up for the songs at their daughters' weddings. Grandmothers described their beautiful granddaughters and showed each other photos. They all just wanted to lose enough weight to fit into their outfits and make it through the wedding reception disco.

Seventeen women, all spurring each other on, and telling each others' futures. "I used to be able to dance and bend like you," one told me. "Now look at me." Of course, now I understand what she was saying. I have not moved like that in seven years.

Everyone is lonely and angry and afraid of their body's failure. Some of the more bitter ones also use marriage to relate their disappointments — the husbands who failed to support their aching bodies and refuse to understand.

He doesn't stop coming over and serenading my table. It is often 'Moon River'. He is always looking at me. I stop wanting to eat there, but we are stuck on an island. There is nowhere else to go.

I become scared of the long corridor between dining hall and thermal tunnel. What if he follows? The lift is so dark and silent.

One day in the bathtub I find a way to leave my body. I fill it so deep with water, I cannot see my own shoulders. I forget to balance it against the wall, but the volume of water holds it firm.

It is hot. I lean back and spread my legs over the inflatable rim. I tilt my head back. Without meaning to, I find myself elevated. I am three feet above the floor before I realise that I'm still conscious.

One day I leave the bathtub running and it overflows.

At first, I do not see the water, only the absence of anything dry.

Water floods the bathroom, piling up around the toilet and the pedal bin in the corner. My small pile of clothes is soaked through. I leave the bathroom naked. Water follows me, spreading out over the hall. It warps the floorboards. My entire home is filling with a slow, seeping shine. I slip, and feel myself falling. Under the kitchen table, I see no distinction between polished water and glistening floor.

My head hurts. I lean my cheek to the floor. As soon as the side of my lip brushes the surface, the reflection begins to make more sense: tepid water, then hard, polished wood. I focus on the line between soft water and hard floor, trying to understand how the liquid has followed me. My tongue falls out, tasting diluted shampoo and sawdust.

I hadn't been aware of the dips in my living room floor previously, but here I am, lying sideways in a hollow. I think again of how liquid bends to the shape of the container in which it is held. I bend my face, spread my wet nostrils and exhale into the water. My tongue hangs loose. Hair trails over me in damp strands. My eyes unfocus. I become as flaccid as I possibly can.

Still, I feel the floor resisting. Subtle arches of wood laminate push at my jaw. I become aware of my own stiffness: my firm buttocks, a spiking knee. Attempting to become water has highlighted something of my hardness. No matter how much my flesh ripples, underneath it I am all angles. The thought horrifies me. If I could, I would let my eyeballs fall out of my soft skull and plop into puddles on the floor.

≈

Union workers refuse to touch the sickness. Rats die. It clogs up a vital reservoir. Clouds of sickness float upwards in tiny particles and hang over the city; an orange fog that makes it difficult for anyone to see where they're going. Tides change. Little droplets of sickness rain down over notable landmarks, melting them like candlesticks in an old French restaurant. Big Ben has the sickness! The Shard has the sickness! Streets swirl. Children splash their feet in it.

I am beginning to understand that my body isn't fluid at all.

It was hard in the water today, really hard. There were exercises I simply couldn't do. The physio was asking me to push my hands down on a float in the water and they were shaking and spasming and I had to say, "No, I can't do that." We had to keep adapting everything. Yesterday I went on an exercise bike and a cross-trainer and I walked, with some very positive encouragement from my land physiotherapist. It was too much. I thought I'd give it a go because the physiotherapist had been very optimistic about my progress. I liked the idea of feeling positive. My heart rate increased. I felt myself release a load of endorphins. But I know my body and I knew it was too much — and it *was* too much.

I am exhausted this morning. I'm struggling to sit up. My knee is hot and swollen.

I'm doing all this exercise, but I have all these underlying fears. Am I making the right decisions? Am I being given the right advice? You go through life as a chronically ill person with so many different people who have so many different opinions about how your treatment should be. They're not always useful or right. You have to build your own narrative and your own sense of what feels appropriate. You have to learn to trust your body to tell you what's working. But that's hard too, when your body keeps changing the rules.

I'm a week and a half into the programme and I probably have to start listening to my body more than the physiotherapist. I have to relax, to allow the pain to be there so I can explore what the impact of having the pain might be. Does it go away? Do I recover? Do I swell up? The question is always, "Is the pain trying to tell you something? Or is it just pain?"

It's weird. I feel I'm becoming less and less coherent in these recordings because I'm so very tired. I can't keep a thought in my head, I can barely keep eye contact with myself in the mirror.

I'm at the midpoint now. I'd better be careful that I don't tip myself over.

One foot of the bathtub has disappeared. When it first worked loose, I spent weeks anxiously replacing it every time I went to brush my teeth or pee. Then we got used to it, and just stepped around it. Now it is gone. I look down into the plastic frame that was holding it in place. It is hollow and dark inside. Not many weeks later, the hole is thick with fungus.

Hello, hello. It's Week Two, Day Four of my time in the Sanatorium. It's another day where I didn't go in the water too much. I had land-physio first thing. I was late because I was tired. Lucy, my carer, was helping me to get ready quite a lot, but I still didn't remember all the essential things you need to go downstairs. We did quite a lot of physiotherapy, some really intense exercises with big Pilates balls. I have one at home, so I was excited about being able to keep this up beyond rehab. But it was really hard. My arms were spasming with how hard it was.

I don't know if that's good for someone with a connective tissue disorder. I've seen other people work that hard. I know that's a thing, but pushing so much has never ended well for me. All my muscles feel very tense and shaky. My physio encouraged me to go to the gym this evening and cycle. She thinks I shouldn't use the cross-trainer anymore.

Today, I haven't even lain around in the big bath. I'm meant to do it three times a day. I had my first day off from three times a day on Tuesday. It's harder to work it in when you've got land-physio and cold-cream-pack therapy as well, which you have to be dry for. They put this icy magic healing cream on my swollen joints every few days. The cold sensation lasts for a few hours. It's unnerving getting into the warm water afterwards. The sensation of having cold shoulders and knees in a very warm bath is uncomfortable and confusing. So I end up skipping a few rounds of the thermal water on cold-pack days.

The gym where I do land-physio is on my floor. It's about a minute's walk away, so I thought, *OK, let's walk there, that's what I've been told to do*. I've still got another week to correct things if I do collapse. So I did just that. I did the land-physio. I went for underwater massage and a cold-cream pack. Then I went slowly back to the room. What did I do? I stared at a screen for a long time. I watched reruns of *Friends*. Anything new is too much. I can only watch things that don't challenge me.

I really could do with having a bath now, but I don't trust that I have the energy to change my clothes again, put on a swimsuit and go through the steps of getting dressed and undressed and drying myself as well, and then going to dinner and eating. I'm so tired. If it wasn't past 5pm, I'd probably try and take a nap right now. I should maybe have napped in the afternoon instead of watching crap TV. I'm working my core muscles really hard. They hurt. Muscles I didn't think even knew how to work anymore are hurting. Hopefully that's good. I'm hoping it's good. At this point, I honestly don't know.

The tub sits upside down in the bathroom, leering an elephant smile. When it is not filled with water there is nothing to hold it upright. It does not fit neatly into corners. It refuses to sit up straight.

I don't know if I trust the physiotherapist. She's so charmingly optimistic, it's easy to get carried away even when she's pushing me too hard. She seems to think she knows my body better than I do. Sometimes in the sessions I'll start spasming because my muscles are over tired, and eventually she'll notice and let me stop. I feel that stopping before I spasm would be better for me.

It's very hard if someone's telling you, "You could be better. You could have a better life if you walked more today. You could have a better life if you cycled a bit harder. You should still be swimming. You should still be doing this." Today I told her, "My knee's swollen up. My knee's bigger and I'm in pain. I'm limping more." She just said, "Yup, good, OK, go back and do the bike again."

I did the bike for three and a half minutes and that's a huge achievement. Last week, I hadn't done the bike at all. She said, "OK, cool, go back and do it for at least five minutes."

But I just did three and a half and that felt like more than enough. I want to be positive and optimistic, but this isn't my first experience of rehabilitation. I've been disappointed before. I've been broken by it. I know my body and I just don't believe.

I read a book in the bathtub. The cover is pure white. A single drop will ruin it. I play to the tub's advantage, blowing up its lid with chapped lips, poking my arms through its zip holes and balancing the book in dry hands, safely above the surface. The lid immediately sinks. I abandon it and piss in the water. I don't stop reading. I consume everything: footnotes, asterisks, with thanks-tos and this-was-funded-bys.

Once I am spent, I throw the book in the water, letting the words dissolve and stick to my skin. I am dizzy. My tongue skims the surface, scooping up a single word:

BREATHE

I'm so scared of what will happen if I overdo it. Will my immune system play up? Today I'm exactly halfway through. There is as much time left to finish the programme as I've just completed. If I spend all of that pushing too hard, what happens at the end? What happens if I get paralysed again or start hallucinating? Or I'm just so exhausted I can't get myself dressed, and miss an appointment? There are some very real fears. That being said, there's only one more day of exercise to get through and then it's rest at the weekend and I'll make sure I have extra-long baths and try not to do too much on the Sunday, and things like that.

So yeah, either this is going really well and it's meant to feel like this, or I'm about to go over the edge. I don't know which it is anymore. I don't know if I'm doing well at this or if I'm going to kill myself. The potential for it to go wrong is still very real for me. But I cycled four and a half minutes today and I managed half an hour of physiotherapy. It was so hard but I did it. So I don't know. I don't know. Yeah, I don't know.

PART THREE

I lifted a medicine ball because I believed in medicine. Believed, at least, that the problem could be cured by increasing gravity's pull on my putty limbs. I lifted the ball and knew instantly I was wrong. But I held on tight. I moved with the ball. I told myself it would help me.

I lifted it waist-high, already knowing my mistake. But, medicine. I rotated it three times clockwise, three times back. I spent the rest of the day in that heady mix of euphoria and the twitch of muscles that do not like to be woken.

At night I took my medicine. But the ball was stronger. I kept on twitching. Slumber was cold and dead. Pictures did not come into me.

All night I thought of medicine. How, the morning after, I might creep towards the pool to cure this error in exercise judgement, dragging my shoulders just below the surface and turning them three times clockwise, three times back.

At 6 or 7am my beloved awoke. I rolled head-first onto his pillow. I buried my face in his shoulder and breathed his breath, hoping to borrow his stillness. Medicine. Nothing settled. I allowed my lungs to resume their own pace. My limbs were coiled
& revolting
& then

~~~

between wake

I am the shape of my seams
a split line, a floating hallway
nuns sat on my chest & shrieking
tonguelessly in the half-light &
if you were seeking proof we are
falling back on our faith
in multiples, sunbeams have split, they're
wetting the bed. dinner is over. fingers
where they shouldn't be. I've felt it:
statues carved with electric breath

≋

& asleep

& teresa arrived at saint paul's crying
if that's what heaven's like
I've felt it, years of not knowing
where my lips end. I am frictionless &
undesigned for such gravity,
I've felt it. limbless & twined &
pulsing apart, a marionette in tangles
picking between my teeth,
a light-plug factory, garbage trucks
crying milk in the darkness, yawning
into rust

I have not lined up the bathtub drain with the shower plughole. I finger the edges to ply it wider. Water goes everywhere, flooding all the way to the toilet. I am forced to use up all the clean towels to prevent the eruption. Later in the week I confess my bisexuality, but only to the friends who already know. All weekend I enter the bathroom sockless. On Monday the cleaner comes to me in a panic. No matter how long she spends on her knees, she can't scrape milky white tidemarks off the bathroom floor.

〜〜

I think you could sit on any part of Teresa and still not prevent her raptures.

"Try it," she told me. So I sat on her face.

≋

I felt the most spectacular trembling sensation and wanted to weep. And suddenly I saw glorious things inside myself! A sparkling castle, built from a labyrinth of seven mansions. Each mansion is more spectacular than the last. Outside the castle, the ground is littered with serpents and toads.

Hello, this is Abi. It's Week 3, Day 2 of the Sanatorium and I've had enough. I am escaping. It's a bit like *The Prisoner*, that '60s TV show about the ex-spy who gets kidnapped and sent to a secret island in the middle of nowhere. He's never allowed to leave the island. Each week he makes an escape attempt, but there's a big inflatable bubble that chases him and drags him back.

I just scooted out of my room, all wrapped up in EIGHT LAYERS because it's freezing. My snot has formed an icicle already. As I left, the doorman spoke into his walkie-talkie. I swear he was watching me.

It's very dark. I just got completely lost in a field of statues, which is also something that happens in *The Prisoner*. It might be because I've seen it on the telly, but I really think I saw one move.

It would be quite good if a giant plastic bubble did come and retrieve me in a while because it's freezing and I get lost easily.

But it would be nice to escape for long enough to not have to go to dinner tonight. To have one night of not being serenaded and buffeted. It would be nice to get a cup of coffee from somewhere that isn't there. My goal is to cross the bridge and maybe find somewhere to eat.

I don't know if this is a good sign. I'm going stir-crazy. Which means I want to leave. Which means that perhaps my body is coping better. I want to get up and do stuff. Let me tell you, I sure as hell wasn't feeling up to leaving the first week I was here.

I could cry at how beautiful it is along the river. I haven't felt so free in a long time.

~~~

The hardest thing about entering the castle is that it's hard to tell which mansion you're in. The ones closest to heaven are filled with light. The ones on the perimeter sometimes let a snake in.

I forgot to mention it sooner, but towards the end of last week I started shitting blood again. Today several people congratulated me on my notable weight loss.

≋

Sometimes you think you've made it to the final mansion. You are full of incandescent harmonies. Then you open your eyes and realise that the floor is vibrating with snakes.

The first time I started trying to walk again, an occupational therapist sat in my front room with a worksheet and stories of my fellow comrades who had pushed too hard. We took it one step at a time, a carer following behind me with my wheelchair like a royal train. I focused on lifting the front of my feet and placing the heel on the ground, counting each step.

We increased five steps per week, working our way up from 10 to 50 in the space of two months. My progress was dizzying. I had to be careful not to get carried away. At the 50 mark I transfered my walking to my college corridors, proudly walking into my classroom, before climbing back into my wheelchair seat.

One day we decided to go even further, relegating the wheelchair to the corner, making it face the wall. The price of sitting in a less supportive chair cost all my energy. I spent the next week stuck on my back.

Eventually I found I had reached a plateau. I was ready to be well again and live my life. I invested all my savings on a therapy which states on every page, *This Is Not a Miracle Cure,* but also claims that you will be living a full and active life again within three days.

≋

Tripping over a snake is always dangerous. You might find yourself back at the beginning again, limping your way to the first mansion with a wounded knee.

Stop. Do you want to go into the pit or do you want to move towards the life you love? I want to move towards the life I love. *Well done, you are a powerful genius, you can do anything you want and I'm with you every step of the way.* Thank you. *What do you want?* I want to be as strong as a mountain / I want to be as full of relentless energy as a babbling brook / I want to walk as easily as a panther prowling through the forest at night. *How are you going to do that?* I'm going to do that by taking myself back to a time I felt strong as a mountain / as full of relentless energy as a babbling brook / by imagining what it's like to walk as easily as a panther prowling through the forest at night.

Well done, you are a powerful genius. You can now take a step towards the life you love.

I started walking more and more. I took a bus by myself. I swam across a pool and although I had to stop several times to re-hypnotise myself, I cried with joy. One day I was carrying my own weight across town to meet a friend who works in a department store. Out of nowhere, I found my feet stepping forwards, one step in front of the other, without me having to concentrate. As if it were nothing.

Three months later I step into a bathtub. Both my ankles snap.

This is Abi. It is Week 3 Day 4 of being in the Sanatorium. I think I've probably skipped a few days because I've not been in the mood to talk. I've been having fun. Today I sneaked out. I didn't have dinner in the big hotel. It's been snowing here today and I was thinking of meeting my care assistant, Lucy, for dinner in the city and then she said, "It's too cold, you shouldn't really go out in this weather."

So I said "OK" and then I put on all my clothes and sneaked out anyway. It was fucking cold. I brought my warm blankets and every layer of warm clothes I possibly could. I was still cold and had to keep my legs moving so my knee didn't freeze over. When I got into the town, I texted her. *Surprise! I'm in the town.* I would have been really happy to sit in a café or a restaurant by myself and read my book, but she said, *Look, I'm 10 minutes away, let's have dinner.* That was really nice. It felt like a real human thing to do and not about wellness or hotels. Yeah, it was good, it was nice to get away from here.

My knee definitely stiffens up in the cold, I have to be a bit careful about that. But it felt like a worthwhile compromise. Having been through three weeks of therapy, I feel like my knee isn't going to miraculously recover. I'm always going to have pain in this one knee, but that's very, very different from having pain in one knee and two swollen-up feet and constantly going to hospital for steroid shots and being unable to sit up straight and all of those things. The amount of physiotherapy I've done has helped my back recover from constant pain. It's given me a small moment of rest, to lie in warm water and feel the embrace of weightlessness, that lack of gravity, for a few hours. The freedom of movement that being in the water gives me is life-changing. I hope I can keep swimming when I get home.

I had my last land-physiotherapy session today. Yesterday my knee was hurting quite a lot. During physio I said, "Look, my knee's really hurting." And, for the first time, the physiotherapist amended my exercises to take the pain into account. She stopped saying, "You can do everything," and started saying, "Don't do it if it hurts."

So that was helpful. It was nice to have that sort of closure before I leave, the sense that my instinct is right: if something is causing me intense pain, it's probably not a good exercise to keep doing. That's been causing anxiety the whole way through this. Pushing through sharp pain doesn't seem to help anyone. Now I know I don't have to, I can stick to a range of exercises which don't trigger it.

So today was my last day. Again, the physio was really kind. She didn't push my painful knee too hard. She listened when I said it hurt. We reduced things, and she made a much better effort at showing me how to adapt my exercises to the pain, rather than not believing me. Then she left me with this message:

"Don't stop," she said. "Keep on exercising."

She said, "Make sure you exercise every day."

"Yup," I said. "I sure will. Now I've had some time to rehabilitate, I'll definitely do that."

"Get rid of your wheelchair," she said.

"Stop thinking of your wheelchair as a solution," she said.

"You don't need that stuff."

"You're not sick," she said. "You've just got a little problem."

I have not reached the point where I'm walking for two minutes a day yet. I was hopeful last week, but that has not happened.

The second time we try again at walking, I am an inpatient on a rehab programme with the NHS. Other patients with my condition talk about how many times they've also tried.

The physiotherapist tells me to stop moving so much and focus instead on my buttocks. "You're using the wrong muscles," he tells me. Every day I have to clench my glutes until I am strong enough to stand up straight.

They encourage me to try walking through water, but the chlorine burns my urethra and I end up with a kidney infection.

By week three I have moved too much. There is a cricket in the radiator and all night I can hear it singing. There is always a woman, awake in the darkness, calling to a nurse because she's in so much pain.

I was in the waiting room before underwater massage this morning. A woman sat down next to me. I've seen her around but we've never spoken. She asked how my trip had been and then told me about her own experience. She's another one who comes every year. I would guess that she's in her 60s.

She kept saying this phrase I can't get out of my head: "I deserve this."

"I worked hard all my life," she said.

"I was always very careful to save."

"I deserve this."

"I deserve this."

Then she asked if I was planning to come back again next year. I said that I'd love to come back but I'd have to work out how to pay for it. I explained that the trip was part of a research grant for an arts organisation. I made a joke about how there are only so many times you can research your own rehabilitation. I thought she'd laugh but instead she just looked me up and down and said: "Don't you WORK?"

Today I missed a therapy by mistake. They were all booked too close together and I needed a rest after physio and lost track of time. It was a massage. I haven't made any effort to arrange another one. I'm starting to get exhausted from being touched by strangers.

Things I'm going to miss: the warm baths. I really wish my house had an actual bath. I have an inflatable bathtub, but it's not the same. I'll miss having thermal water to lie in when I'm in pain. That's a real blessing. If I'd just come and had that, I would have been grateful. I am going to miss having physiotherapists tell me how to move every day. It's going to be really hard to work out how much I can do by myself and where my natural stopping point is. I'm probably going to have to keep a diary for a few months of how much exercise I do every day, what was too much, what was too little, what hurt, what felt good, what's compatible with my actual lived existence. I'm curious about that. We'll see. We'll see how it goes.

Today I completed my rehabilitation programme. I was buzzing. I didn't know what to do with myself, but I got back to my hotel room and I realised I hadn't ever fully appreciated the joy of being in a hotel. I put Sylvester on the radio: "You make me feel mighty real."

First I danced, then I looked at the bed and thought, *Why haven't I bounced on the bed yet?* That's the most obvious, logical thing to do in a hotel. So I did.

Very, very, very quickly I realised that I have quite a horrible joint pain and a busted knee. That's why I've been in rehab for the past month. It really hurt. That was stupid. Sorry, knee.

Hello, this is Abi. It is now the end of my stay in the Sanatorium. It's Week Four Day One. I'm going home tomorrow. Yesterday I had my final massage as a special, last-day treat. I got a bumhole massage. She didn't quite part my cheeks like my first-day initiation ceremony, but it was close. A full circle.

It's my last night on the NHS ward and I'm excited to be going home. As a farewell treat, I braid my neighbour's hair. Another patient warns us that we'll overtire ourselves, but we ignore her. We stay up late telling each other secrets. Then we kiss each other's cheeks and go to bed.

In the ward next to us, a man is withdrawing from morphine. He screams and cries. This hospital used to be a sanatorium for convalescent soldiers. Sometimes I think about the ones who did not make it.

≈

And then they are watching me. Three pale soldiers.
They are in damp green uniform. The haunted eyes.
Their wooden crutches. They smell of animal fat and
petrol.

≋

Breathe in. Breathe out. Hold onto the bed. Breathe
in. Breathe out. I can't feel my hands. I do not want
this. I call for the nurse.

≋

The nurse appears beside me. She is watching but says nothing. I can smell her perfume. She climbs on top of me and leans in. I can taste her lipstick. I try to re-mind her of the 16 women on either side of my bed.

≋

Soldiers are summoning me. I start climbing out of my body but I try to fight it. I can feel my legs grow numb. It just seems so unlikely to be leaving my body — here — in a hospital bed. I try to keep myself moving, tethered to the earth. I want to feel my feet on the ground so I swing my body around, but my legs aren't where I think they are. I end up face down on the floor, ghosts crowding over me.

St Teresa of Ávila takes a pebble shaped like an egg
and forces it into me. I climax so hard it breaks stone.

〜〜〜

The next day I am barely able to shuffle. I spend the next year falling in and out of the wrong world.

Tonight, the double bassist is particularly attentive, stretching his head around the pillars to catch me. I am seated next to a pair of old German women who warble along to the operatic numbers. They tip the violinist instead of blushing and dropping their gaze. Three small girls in matching grey pinafores pinned with delicate pleats hold hands. In this crowd, the orchestra are harmless but less impressive.

I run into a lady I've seen at breakfast. She fell down a crevice in the Pyrenees and broke everything. She is a nurse to rich aristocracy, she tells me, but even so, I cannot work out how she affords two houses and £17,000 worth of treatment to fix her teeth. I tell her she does not look 60, a truth owed to thick blonde pigtails and the brand new molars. She displays them proudly, gnashing at everyone. She agrees the orchestra are lecherous bastards. We go for a drink in the 1920s bar. She has taken a lot of morphine.

Another woman joins us, a Ukrainian fibromyalgia patient called Eva. Pyrenees Morphine New Tooth Woman is British to the core, all brassy hair and shimmering lipstick. We order G&Ts and laugh too loud: Brits. We talk about men. The Brit married a young rugby player who blessed her with two 6'7" sons. She cannot retain females. She miscarried six of them, including a pair of beautiful twins at six months. After she divorced the rugby player, she shacked up with a millionaire professor. They are 12 years apart in age and he is boring. "BORING," she cries, over and over again. "All he wants to do is read." She tells me he likes his women but is crap in bed. "And he can't have affairs where we live," she cackles. "We're surrounded by mountains and sheep."

One month after the Brit fell down the Pyrenees crevice, her sister came out to nurse her. At 7am, a little tipsy, she (the sister), dressed only in red fur coat and transparent negligee, crept into the cellar for firewood and champagne. She fell, and broke her leg. The bone split her skin. The Brit says the air ambulance are tired of flying out to this lonely old house in the mountains. The sister also has fibromyalgia. She manages it with skunk.

Eva's perspective on men is different; they are allowed to demand sex, but only for something in exchange. Last night she went for dinner with a 74-year-old academic. He invited her to bed. She refused, but in the daytime, as they solved a Sudoku together, she let him hold her hand. He slowly ran his fingers between her knuckles, but the only reimbursement was beer.

We order a nightcap. The women chastise me for using codeine. "There's an opioid epidemic," the Ukrainian tells me. "Why aren't you taking morphine?" asks the Brit.

Back in London, I try to maintain the exercises that the physi-otherapist asked me to complete in water. A pedal. A squat. On earth my knee begins grinding. It sounds like exploding grapes. A sharp pain.

Hi, this is Abi. It's been one month since I arrived home from the Sanatorium. Yesterday, I was finally well enough to go to a party. It's the first time I've seen any of my friends in over a month. I wore platform shoes, which I'm not supposed to do. I taped up my knee, which I'm not supposed to do because I get a really bad allergic reaction to the knee tape. But I felt like it might be worth it for one night. I had enough strength in my other leg to lean on, to relieve the pain in the bad one. So I was able to stand up for longer and climb some stairs.

It felt really nice to be included. I also didn't have the usual feeling that haunts me: *I wish I'd been able to stay longer, I wish I fitted in, I wish I felt part of things.*

I felt like myself, which I haven't for a long time.

Everyone at the party kept saying, "You look really well." But I'm limping quite heavily. That's a hard thing to explain. Walking is a sign of how well you're doing and being able to walk means, "Oh yeah, you're coping." Not being able to walk means, "No, you're not coping." There's no space for a grey area of, "Wow, you've made significant improvements, but they're very internal." I can sit up straighter and I feel less pain, but I still can't walk very well. That's a hard thing to explain to people.

I'm not coping very well with any standing-up exercises. My left knee is still behaving badly. It's making all these weird, crunching noises when I try to stretch it or do the things I've been asked to do by my physio. I used Dr Google and it says those crunching noises if you have arthritis aren't that good. That has worried me. I feel a lot stronger. My core is a lot stronger. My hips, my thighs and glutes and stuff are all firing and I seem to be able to maintain and sustain exercise, but nonetheless, my knee is still pretty fucked. So I still can't walk. That's been a really interesting thing to think about. What do I do about that?

One day the bathtub finds a permanent space in the corner of my bathroom.

I make no attempt to disguise the mould.

I start paying extravagant prices in order to be able to do enough work to pay for all the therapies I'm doing in order to work. I stop being able to pay my phone bill.

One day my care assistant offers to run me a bath and I realise I am too disgusted by the tub to get in.

END

A year after attending the Sanatorium, I am moving more slowly than ever. The doctor informs me that my medication hasn't been working after all. There is a more effective and less harmful medication available, she tells me, but it's very expensive. I do not qualify for a prescription. I ask if there is any way I can appeal this decision, given the difficulty I am having juggling multiple musculoskeletal complaints. She tells me that health economists would consider my range of diagnoses to be 'statistically improbable' and therefore reject my application. I ask her if she has any reason to doubt my diagnoses. She says no.

Oh Saint Teresa!

I am placed on a cheaper drug. It is bright orange and smells like petrol. I ask a nurse about the side effects listed on my medication, such as nausea and liver failure. She says that side effects only happen to people who are worried about the side effects.

Teresa, floating on your back in ecstasy.

Almost immediately I can feel the change in my body. My feet shrink until I can fit into normal trainers. I go on holiday and find I am able to walk into the sea every day without flaring. I stop wearing my knee-support bandage. I find that I am able to perform acts of lovemaking more frequently. I am able to hold myself up for long enough to attend a public swimming pool. A friend tells me they have never seen me move so freely.

Teresa, gargling clouds and holy water.

The side effects, however, are too much to bear. I become very dizzy and start forgetting important facts. I miss hospital appointments and forget how to finish sentences. My brain fog is so thick that sometimes I struggle to remember how to cross the road. My clothes smell like burning rubber and it takes me a few weeks to realise that the smell is coming from my skin. I itch terribly. The itching wakes me at night.

Teresa who wails, face crumpled in triangles. Teresa, dressed in a wet-look wedding dress, damp hair hanging around her shoulders. Saint Teresa, refuser of bread.

On the medicine packet they warn that itching might be the symptom of a damaged liver. When I tell her I'm struggling to function mentally, the doctor tells me I'm being too hard on myself. She wonders if the itching might be a symptom of anxiety.

Slap me, Teresa, slap me with your coldest ocean.

I've been waking up in the night and screaming. Apparently I see monsters in my sleep. I've seen creatures watching me from the bed: a spider plant, a pigeon, one of the Pokémon you get everywhere on London streets. Hans is woken time and time again by my screams. I am terrified by what my body is becoming.

Teresa, drown me with your wet tears and damp armpits and thick yellow breast excretions and cloudy piss.

I am one of the more privileged ones and still I'm screaming. God, it would be so nice just to dissolve into nothing and wash up onto a lonely beach. Or to expand and keep expanding, to form into vapour and never have to leave the sky.

I beg you, Teresa, for a sharp hard rain to fall over my stomach, vicious little pinpricks that fail to pierce the membrane of my skin. Bless me with this, Teresa: the opposite of chronic pain.

May I remain submerged until my fingers turn to prunes, the prunes curl up, the curls form leaves. Eventually may I have no need for hands at all.

May I sink through the water, barely needing breath (like an astronaut, swallowing pictures of the sun).

May I crumble into nothing.

May the tide return

and drag me far away

The hydrotherapy pool at Guy's Hospital is one of only four left in London, but the one at Charing Cross is closing down next week. I ask the therapist if she believes this one will close too. "No," she says. "We've kept it open by running private sessions."

It costs £68 for a 30-minute one-to-one induction session. Once you have been to one, you are allowed to go to a three-to-one session (£20) or freeform hydrotherapy (no instructor, 8 patients in the pool at a time): £8. It still adds up. I ask the physiotherapist if I could get a free NHS referral instead. "You might be able to," she says, "but then again you might not. You'd have to be referred back to physiotherapy. That's at least a 6-week wait. Then they will assess you. If they refer you onto hydrotherapy, you'll get 4 sessions."

She tells me about a patient she worked with at another hospital. They worked together for 5 years. He began on a stretcher, and he left on foot. "He's not playing football or anything," she says, "but he's walking around and living his life." For a year, their goal was just to get him to sit up straight, at first for 3 minutes, slowly building up to 15. I think about my 4 free sessions in the water.

The hospital pool is wide and shallow, with an elaborate system of very low steps zigzagging up and back into the water. I like the tiles around the edges: a Malibu-sunset pattern. The man who booked me in warned me to bring moisturiser for afterwards because it's got a higher-than-average chlorine content. I barrier-cream everything carefully beforehand, even my legs, but it still stings. I worry about how long I'll manage to keep this up before I'm awake all night with itching and cystitis.

I move into the pool, listing my symptoms and diagnoses off the top of my head. The physiotherapist invites me to warm up. We take small deliberate steps across the water. She explains that the power of hydrotherapy is that the water supports your body weight so you don't have to. Everything feels very familiar. I wonder if what I've learned about chronic illness, more than anything, is that it's a constant cycle. You fall apart, then you try your best to rebuild again. I wonder what would happen if I stopped trying. She asks me to climb up and down the steps and suggests that I tell her when I've done enough. "You know your body best," she says, and I nod in agreement.

I am beginning again.

THANKS

This book would not be possible without the input of my many opulent & beautiful muses: Emily Cooper, Andrea Mongenie, Nathalie Pinole, Amy Thomas, Ruby Maclennan, Marjam Lohne, Megan Dalton, Kate Adori, Martha PW, Avery Curran, Caitlin Doherty, every single person in the Jellicle Chat 4 Jellicats Whatsapp group (Fleur, thanks for letting me borrow your name), Mary Slattery, Ella Harrison, Elena Colman, Kate Cheka, Laura Lulika, Leah Clements, Romily Alice Walden, Anna Ulrikke Andersen, Jamie Hale, Miss Jacqui, Lulu Nunn, Rosie Hayes, David Turner, Lizzy Turner, Andrew Goldman, Jackie Hagan, St Teresa of Ávila.

Tremendous gratitude to every teacher, mentor & advocate who has made space for my Abi-ness: Robert Stanley, Jennie Rejmann, Christianne Zschommler, Geoff Faulkner, Wesley Freeman-Smith, Nathan Penlington, Niall O'Sullivan, Tim Wells, Roddy Lumsden, Kev, Mary Newbould, Michael Hrebeniak, Gemma Seltzer, James Trevelyan, Sarah Sanders, Sara Dziadik, Shape Arts, Arts Council England, the wonderful Kate Wilkinson & Rosie Dunnett at Penned in the Margins. Wayne Holloway-Smith, thanks for encouragement & wisdom at all the right times. To every teacher who ever said "Remember me when you write your first book", I have not forgotten — look me up!

Many thanks to the National Health Service for keeping me alive. Sorry I've been critical. I love you.

Special thanks to Tessa Young, Marjorie Lee, Grandpa Bunty, Rachel Walters, Jane Barker, Ola Zielinska, Lucy Clarke, Danielchka Machova, Emmi Anderwall, Korpo Galakpai, Christabel Bradley and Simon Barraclough.

Tom Chivers, THANK YOU so much for taking such a leap with me. Nick Murray, thanks for being such a fantastic artist, producer & friend, & for drawing the illustrations that accompany this book. Dad, sorry you had to read the first line of this book in a Wetherspoons with no warning. Debs, Guy, Hugh and Emma, thanks for being there to witness Dad reading the first line. Pippa Palmer, I would not be the writer I am without having my mum as first reader. Ollie Palmer, you are the Chas to my Dave.

My beloved G, I cannot find the words. Thank you for our small and quiet world. I am so glad we found each other.

ENDNOTES

The wording on page 157 is taken from The Lightning Process, designed by Phil Parker.

The image of a wet-look wedding dress (and the imagery surrounding female wetness) on pages 200 to 206 are taken from designer Di Petsa's project on Wetness, which has been a huge influence on the writing of this book.

FURTHER READING

Teresa of Ávila, *The Interior Castle* (1577), *The Life of Saint Teresa of Ávila by Herself* (1588).
Johanna Hedva, 'Sick Woman Theory' (2016); *On Hell* (2018).

Instagram: @crutches_and_spice @invalid__art
              @ablezine   @obligatory.purgatory
              @hot.crip   @paid.technologies
              @star_seeded   @dipetsa
              @femzinelondon   @aaron___philip
              @thewhitepube   @mia.mingus